真棒
ZHĒN BÀNG! 3

Character Practice Book

2nd Edition

Senior Advisor

王昭華 Margaret M. Wong

Director of International Education / Chinese Instructor
Breck School, Minneapolis, MN

Writers

韩磊 Henry Han

EMC Publishing®

ST. PAUL, MINNESOTA

D1279076

Associate Publisher
Alex Vargas

Interior Designers
Aiko Chao

Text Designer
Ryan Hamner

Cover Designer
Leslie Anderson

Production Specialist
Ryan Hamner

Care has been taken to verify the accuracy of information presented in this book. However, the authors, editors, and publisher cannot accept responsibility for Web, e-mail, newsgroup, or chat room subject matter or content, or for consequences from application of the information in this book, and make no warranty, expressed or implied, with respect to its content.

We have made every effort to trace the ownership of all copyrighted material and to secure permission from copyright holders. In the event of any question arising as to the use of any material, we will be pleased to make the necessary corrections in future printings. Thanks are due to the aforementioned authors, publishers, and agents for permission to use the materials indicated.

ISBN 978-0-82198-830-5 (print)

875 Montreal Way
St. Paul, MN 55102
Email: educate@emcp.com
Website: www.emcschool.com

Printed in the United States of America

26 25 24 23 22 21   2 3 4 5 6 7 8 9 10

Table of Contents

120 Characters

Traditional Radical Chart—The 214 Traditional Radicals

NOTE: Radicals are listed according to the number of strokes.

1	1	一	one		39	子	child		77	止	stop
	2	丨	down stroke		40	宀	roof		78	歹	evil
	3	丶	a point		41	寸	inch		79	殳	kill
	4	丿	left stroke		42	小	small		80	毋(母)	do not
	5	乙	bent		43	尢	lame		81	比	compare
	6	亅	hook		44	尸	corpse		82	毛	hair
2	7	二	two		45	屮	sprout		83	氏	family
	8	亠	a cover		46	山	mountain		84	气	air
	9	人(亻)	man		47	巛(巜川)	stream	**4**	85	水(氵)	water
	10	儿	man		48	工	work		86	火(灬)	fire
	11	入	enter		49	己	self		87	爪(爫)	claws
	12	八	eight		50	巾	napkin		88	父	father
	13	冂	borders		51	干	shield		89	爻	change
	14	冖	to cover		52	幺	tiny		90	爿	a frame
	15	冫	ice		53	广	shelter		91	片	a strip
	16	几	table		54	廴	move on		92	牙	tooth
	17	凵	receptacle		55	廾	joined hands		93	牛	ox
	18	刀(刂)	knife		56	弋	a dart		94	犬(犭)	dog
	19	力	strength		57	弓	a bow		95	玄	dark
	20	勹	wrap		58	彐(彑)	pig's hand		96	玉(王)	jade
	21	匕	spoon		59	彡	feathery		97	瓜	melon
	22	匚	basket		60	彳	to pace		98	瓦	tilt
	23	匸	box		61	心(忄)	heart		99	甘	sweet
	24	十	ten		62	戈	spear		100	生	produce
	25	卜	to divine		63	戶	door		101	用	use
	26	卩(㔾)	seal		64	手(扌)	hand		102	田	field
	27	厂	cliff		65	支	branch		103	疋(⺪)	bolt of cloth
	28	厶	private		66	攴(攵)	tap		104	疒	sick
	29	又	also		67	文	writing	**5**	105	癶	back to back
3	30	口	mouth		68	斗	measure		106	白	white
	31	囗	enclosure		69	斤	axe		107	皮	skin
	32	土	earth	**4**	70	方	square		108	皿	plate
	33	士	scholar		71	旡(无)	not		109	目	eye
	34	夂	follow		72	日	sun		110	矛	lance
	35	夊	walk		73	曰	speak		111	矢	arrow
	36	夕	evening		74	月	moon		112	石	stone
	37	大	big		75	木	wood		113	示(礻)	spirit
	38	女	woman		76	欠	owe		114	禸	to track

真棒 Character Practice Book 3

5	115	禾	grain		153	豸	retile	10	191	鬥	fight
	116	穴	cave		154	貝	shell		192	鬯	wine
	117	立	erect		155	赤	red		193	鬲	caldron
	118	竹（ ⺮ ）	bamboo		156	走	walk		194	鬼	ghost
	119	米	rice		157	足（⻊ ）	foot	11	195	魚	fish
	120	糸（ 纟 ）	silk		158	身	body		196	鳥	bird
	121	缶	earthenware	7	159	車	cart		197	鹵	salt
	122	网（ 罒 ）	net		160	辛	bitter		198	鹿	deer
	123	羊	sheep		161	辰	time		199	麥	wheat
	124	羽	feathers		162	辵（辶）	stop & go		200	麻	hemp
	125	老（ 耂 ）	old		163	邑（ 阝 ）	city	12	201	黃	yellow
	126	而	and		164	酉	new wine		202	黍	millet
	127	耒	plough		165	釆	separate		203	黑	black
	128	耳	ear		166	里	village		204	黹	embroidery
	129	聿	brush		167	金	metal	13	205	黽	toad
	130	肉（月）	flesh		168	長	long		206	鼎	tripod
	131	臣	officer		169	門	gate		207	鼓	drum
6	132	自	self		170	阜（阝 ）	plenty		208	鼠	rodent
	133	至	reach	8	171	隶	reach to	14	209	鼻	nose
	134	臼	a mortar		172	隹	a bird		210	齊	even
	135	舌	tongue		173	雨	rain	15	211	齒	teeth
	136	舛	opposed		174	青	azure	16	212	龍	dragon
	137	舟	boat		175	非	false		213	龜	tortoise
	138	艮	a limit		176	面	face	17	214	龠	flute
	139	色	color		177	革	rawhide				
	140	艸（ ⺾ ）	grass		178	韋	leather				
	141	虍	tiger		179	韭	leek				
	142	虫	insect		180	音	sound				
	143	血	blood	9	181	頁	heading				
	144	行	go, do		182	風	wind				
	145	衣（ 衤 ）	clothes		183	飛	fly				
	146	襾（ 西 覀 ）	cover		184	食（飠 ）	eat				
	147	見	see		185	首	head				
	148	角	horn		186	香	fragrance				
7	149	言	words		187	馬	horse				
	150	谷	valley		188	骨	bone				
	151	豆	platter	10	189	高	high				
	152	豕	pig		190	髟	long hair				

Simplified Radical Chart—The 186 Simplified Radicals

NOTE: Radicals are listed according to the number of strokes.

1	1	丶	*a point*		38	辶	*stop & go*		75	火	*fire*
	2	一	*one*		39	工	*work*		76	心	*heart*
	3	丨	*down stroke*		40	土	*earth*		77	户	*door*
	4	丿	*left stroke*		41	士	*scholar*		78	礻	*spirit*
	5	乙 (乁乚)	*bent*		42	艹	*n/a*[1]		79	王	*king*
2	6	亠	*a cover*		43	大	*big*		80	韦	*leather*
	7	冫	*ice*		44	廾	*joined hands*		81	木	*wood*
	8	冖	*to cover*		45	尢	*lame*		82	犬	*dog*
	9	讠	*words*		46	寸	*inch*		83	歹	*evil*
	10	二	*two*		47	弋	*a dart*		84	车	*cart*
	11	十	*ten*		48	扌	*hand*		85	戈	*spear*
	12	厂	*cliff*		49	小 (⺌)	*small*		86	比	*compare*
	13	匚	*box*		50	口	*mouth*		87	瓦	*tile*
	14	卜	*to divine*		51	囗	*enclosure*		88	止	*stop*
	15	刂	*knife*		52	巾	*napkin*		89	攴	*tap*
	16	冂	*borders*		53	山	*mountain*		90	日	*sun*
	17	八 (丷)	*eight*		54	彳	*to pace*		91	曰	*speak*
	18	人 (入)	*man; enter*		55	彡	*feathery*		92	贝	*shell*
	19	亻	*man*	**3**	56	夕	*evening*	**4**	93	见	*see*
	20	勹	*wrap*		57	夂	*walk*		94	父	*father*
	21	儿	*man*		58	犭	*dog*		95	牛 (牜)	*ox*
	22	几 (几)	*table*		59	饣	*eat*		96	手	*hand*
	23	厶	*private*		60	彐 (⺕彑)	*pig's heads*		97	毛	*hair*
	24	又	*also*		61	尸	*corpse*		98	气	*air*
	25	辵	*move on*		62	己 (已)	*self*		99	夊	*follow*
	26	卩	*seal*		63	弓	*a bow*		100	片	*a strip*
	27	阝	*plenty*		64	屮	*sprout*		101	斤	*axe*
	28	阝	*city*		65	女	*woman*		102	爪 (爫)	*claws*
	29	凵	*receptacle*		66	幺	*tiny*		103	月	*moon*
	30	刀 (⺈)	*knife*		67	子 (孑)	*man*		104	欠	*owe*
	31	力	*strength*		68	纟	*silk*		105	风	*wind*
	32	氵	*water*		69	马	*horse*		106	殳	*kill*
	33	忄	*heart*		70	巛	*stream*		107	聿	*n/a*
3	34	宀	*roof*		71	灬	*fire*		108	毋	*do not*
	35	斗 (爿)	*a frame*		72	斗	*measure*		109	水	*water*
	36	广	*shelter*		73	文	*writings*		110	穴	*cave*
	37	门	*gate*		74	方	*square*				

[1] Some radicals in Simplified Chinese are just the component of the character and do not have meanings. For radicals like these, n/a is shown instead of a meaning.

Stroke	#	Char	Meaning	Stroke	#	Char	Meaning	Stroke	#	Char	Meaning
	111	立	*erect*		149	舟	*boat*	12	184	黑	*black*
	112	疒	*sick*	6	150	羽	*feathers*		185	鼠	*mouth*
	113	衤	*clothes*		151	艮	*a limit*	以			
	114	示	*spirit*		152	糸	*silk*	上			
	115	石	*stone*		153	辛	*bitter*		186	鼻	*nose*
	116	龙	*dragon*		154	麦	*wheat*				
	117	业	*n/a*		155	走	*walk*				
	118	目	*eye*		156	赤	*red*				
	119	田	*field*		157	豆	*platter*				
	120	罒	*n/a*		158	酉	*new wine*				
5	121	皿	*plate*		159	辰	*time*				
	122	钅	*mental*	7	160	豕	*pig*				
	123	矢	*arrow*		161	卤	*bittern*				
	124	禾	*grain*		162	里	*village*				
	125	白	*white*		163	足	*foot*				
	126	瓜	*melon*		164	豸	*reptile*				
	127	鸟	*bird*		165	谷	*valley*				
	128	用	*use*		166	采	*separate*				
	129	矛	*lance*		167	身	*body*				
	130	疋（⺪）	*bolt of cloth*		168	角	*horn*				
	131	皮	*skin*		169	青	*azure*				
	132	衣	*clothes*		170	其	*its*				
	133	羊	*sheep*		171	雨	*rain*				
	134	米	*rice*	8	172	齿	*teeth*				
	135	耒	*plough*		173	金	*mental*				
	136	老	*old*		174	隹	*a bird*				
	137	耳	*ear*		175	鱼	*fish*				
	138	臣	*officer*		176	音	*sound*				
	139	西（覀）	*cover*		177	革	*rawhide*				
6	140	页	*heading*	9	178	骨	*bone*				
	141	虍	*tiger*		179	食	*eat*				
	142	虫	*insect*		180	鬼	*ghost*				
	143	缶	*earthenware*	10	181	髟	*long hair*				
	144	舌	*tongue*		182	麻	*hemp*				
	145	竹（⺮）	*bamboo*	11	183	鹿	*deer*				
	146	臼	*a mortar*								
	147	自	*self*								
	148	血	*blood*								

Basic Strokes of Chinese Characters

Names		Strokes	Directions of Strokes	Examples
横 héng (horizontal strokes)		一	一	一 yī
竖 shù (vertical strokes)		丨	丨	十 shí
撇 piě (left-falling strokes)		丿	丿	大 dà
捺 nà (right-falling strokes)		㇏	㇏	人 rén
点 diǎn (dots)		丶	丶	六 liù
提 tí (rising strokes)		㇀	㇀	冰 bīng
钩 gōu (hooks)	竖钩 shù gōu (standing hook)	亅	亅	小 xiǎo
	横钩 héng gōu (fat hook)	㇖	㇖	你 nǐ
	斜钩 xié gōu (slanted hook)	㇂	㇂	代 dài
	卧钩 wò gōu (seeping hook)	㇃	㇃	心 xīn
折 zhé (angle strokes)	竖折 shù zhé (vertical angle)	㇗	㇗	山 shān
	横折 héng zhé (horizontal angle)	㇕	㇕	日 rì
	斜折 xié zhé (slanted angle)	㇚	㇚	女 nǚ

真棒 Character Practice Book 3

Rules of Stroke Order of Chinese Characters

Rules		Examples
1. Horizontal first, then vertical.		十 shí: 一 十
2. First top, then bottom.		二 èr: 一 二
3. Left-slanted first, then right-slanted.		八 bā: 丿 八
4. Left first, then right.		川 chuān: 丿 丿丨 川
5. Center first, then both sides.		小 xiǎo: 亅 丿亅 小
6. When making a dot "丶", write it first if it is positioned on the top or upper-left.		文 wén: 丶 亠 宀 文
7. With "closed" characters, make the outside strokes (left, top, right), then the strokes in the middle, then the bottom stroke that "closes" the character.		回 huí: 丨 冂 冂 同 同 回
8. With semi-closed characters, there are three different stroke orders:	A. Strokes in the middle before surrounding stroke(s).	凶 xiōng: 丿 乂 凶 凶
	B. Surrounding strokes before strokes in the middle.	司 sī: 丁 刁 刁 司 司
	C. Top before middle before lower-left.	匹 pǐ: 一 丆 兀 匹

汉字练习 Hànzì Liànxí / *Character Practice*

A

Radical	Traditional / Simplified	Pinyin / Meaning	Combination / Meaning
	箱		

Stroke Order and Practice Writing

丿 𠂉 𠂉 𥫗 𥫗 𥫗 竺 竻

竻 箱 箱 箱 箱 箱

箱 箱

B

Radical	Traditional / Simplified	Pinyin / Meaning	Combination / Meaning
	活		

Stroke Order and Practice Writing

丶 丶 氵 汇 浐 活 活 活

活 活

真棒 Character Practice Book 3   © EMC Publishing

C

Radical	Traditional / Simplified	Pinyin / Meaning	Combination / Meaning
	擦		

Stroke Order and Practice Writing

一　扌　扌　扩　扩　扩　护　护

护　护　挦　挦　挦　擦　擦　擦

擦　擦

D

Radical	Traditional / Simplified	Pinyin / Meaning	Combination / Meaning
	吸		

Stroke Order and Practice Writing

丨　口　口　叻　吸　吸

吸　吸

E

Radical	Traditional / Simplified	Pinyin / Meaning	Combination / Meaning
	衣		

Stroke Order and Practice Writing

丶 一 ナ オ 衣 衣

衣 衣

F

Radical	Traditional / Simplified	Pinyin / Meaning	Combination / Meaning
	烘		

Stroke Order and Practice Writing

丶 丷 少 火 灯 灶 烘 烘

烘

烘 烘

G

Radical	Traditional / Simplified	Pinyin / Meaning	Combination / Meaning
	拾		

Stroke Order and Practice Writing

一　扌　扌　扩　扴　拴　拴　拾　拾

拾　拾

H

Radical	Traditional	Simplified	Pinyin / Meaning	Combination / Meaning
	臟	脏		

Stroke Order and Practice Writing

丿　刀　月　月　月丶　月冖　胪　胪　脏

脏

脏　脏

I

Radical	Traditional	Simplified	Pinyin / Meaning	Combination / Meaning
	爐	炉		

Stroke Order and Practice Writing

丶 丷 少 火 灯 炉 炉 炉

炉 炉

J

Radical	Traditional	Simplified	Pinyin / Meaning	Combination / Meaning
	淨	净		

Stroke Order and Practice Writing

丶 冫 丷 泸 浄 浄 净

净 净

2 听写 Tīngxiě / Dictation

A ☐ ☐ ☐ ☐ ☐ ☐ ☐ ☐ ☐ ☐ ☐ ☐ ☐ ☐

Pinyin:

B ☐ ☐ ☐ ☐ ☐ ☐ ☐ ☐ ☐ ☐ ☐ ☐ ☐ ☐

Pinyin:

3 翻译 Fānyì / Translation

A Would you be willing to help me clean the windows?

☐ ☐ ☐ ☐ ☐ ☐ ☐ ☐ ☐

☐ ☐ ☐ ☐ ☐ ☐ ☐ ☐ ☐

Pinyin:

B Can you teach me how to use this washing machine?

☐ ☐ ☐ ☐ ☐ ☐ ☐ ☐ ☐

☐ ☐ ☐ ☐ ☐ ☐ ☐ ☐ ☐

Pinyin:

4 阅读 Yuèdú / Reading

房东: 这就是我要出租的房子，进来看看吧，记得把鞋子脱掉(take off)。

王猛: 好的，这个房子很大很干净啊。

房东: 是啊，因为住在这个房子里面的人都会按时(on time)做家务。
　　　　　　　　　　　　　　　　　　　　　　　　　　àn

王猛: 都需要做什么家务呢？

房东: 每天都要收拾好自己的屋子，吃完饭以后要及时清理厨具、洗碗。

　　　　周末的时候大家一起打扫厨房、吸地。

王猛: 请问厨房都有什么电器呢？

房东: 厨房里面有洗碗机、冰箱、炉子、微波炉、烤箱和热水壶。

王猛: 请问在哪儿洗衣服呢？

房东: 洗衣房在楼下，烘干机也在那里，我带你去看看。

名字: _____ 日期: _____

1 汉字练习 Hànzì Liànxí / *Character Practice*

A

Radical	Traditional / Simplified	Pinyin / Meaning	Combination / Meaning
	倒		

Stroke Order and Practice Writing

亻亻亻仁仁仵佢佢倒
倒

倒 倒

B

Radical	Traditional / Simplified	Pinyin / Meaning	Combination / Meaning
	油		

Stroke Order and Practice Writing

丶丶氵氵汩沺油油
油 油

C

Radical	Traditional / Simplified	Pinyin / Meaning	Combination / Meaning
	割		

Stroke Order and Practice Writing

丶 丷 宀 宀 宀 宀 宀 宀 害

害 害 割

割 割

D

Radical	Traditional	Simplified	Pinyin / Meaning	Combination / Meaning
	澆	浇		

Stroke Order and Practice Writing

丶 丶 氵 氵 汋 泆 浅 浇 浇

浇 浇

E

Radical	Traditional / Simplified	Pinyin / Meaning	Combination / Meaning
	草		

Stroke Order and Practice Writing

一　艹　艹　艹　芦　苩　苩　草　草

草　草

F

Radical	Traditional / Simplified	Pinyin / Meaning	Combination / Meaning
	雪		

Stroke Order and Practice Writing

一　厂　戸　雨　雨　雨　雪　雪

雪　雪

雪　雪

G

Radical	Traditional / Simplified	Pinyin / Meaning	Combination / Meaning
	金		

Stroke Order and Practice Writing

丿 人 亼 仐 仐 全 金 金

金	金						

H

Radical	Traditional / Simplified	Pinyin / Meaning	Combination / Meaning
	剪		

Stroke Order and Practice Writing

丶 丷 兰 产 亣 首 首 前 前

剪 剪

剪	剪						

I

Radical	Traditional	Simplified	Pinyin / Meaning	Combination / Meaning
	樹	树		

Stroke Order and Practice Writing

一　十　才　木　权　权　权　树　树

树　树

J

Radical	Traditional	Simplified	Pinyin / Meaning	Combination / Meaning
	葉	叶		

Stroke Order and Practice Writing

丨　口　口　叶

叶　叶

2 听写 Tīngxiě / Dictation

A ☐ ☐ ☐ ☐ ☐ ☐ ☐ ☐ ☐ ☐ ☐ ☐ ☐ ☐

Pinyin:

B ☐ ☐ ☐ ☐ ☐ ☐ ☐ ☐ ☐ ☐ ☐ ☐ ☐ ☐

Pinyin:

3 翻译 Fānyì / Translation

A The kids are outside working in the yard. Some are raking leaves and some are taking out the trash.

☐ ☐ ☐ ☐ ☐ ☐ ☐ ☐ ☐ ☐

☐ ☐ ☐ ☐ ☐ ☐ ☐ ☐ ☐ ☐

Pinyin:

B Dad wants to throw away that plastic waste.

☐ ☐ ☐ ☐ ☐ ☐ ☐ ☐ ☐ ☐

☐ ☐ ☐ ☐ ☐ ☐ ☐ ☐ ☐ ☐

Pinyin:

4 阅读 Yuèdú / Reading

李明： 周末了！天气真好，我们出去做一些室外家务吧！

刘芳： 好啊，院子很脏了，我一直(always)想要打扫一下呢。

李明： 我先去院子里扫落叶，你把那边的花浇一浇。

刘芳： 好的，我把屋子里的垃圾也扔出去吧。

李明： 记得垃圾要分类啊，垃圾桶在院子的西边，可回收桶在院子的东边。

刘芳： 这里还有一摞(stack)报纸，是可以回收的吗？

              luò

李明： 报纸当然可以回收啦。

刘芳： 好，我们整理完院子再一起洗洗车吧，我的白车都变成黑车了。

Unit 1 Review

名字: _____ 日期: _____

1 句子重组 Jùzi Chóngzǔ / Unscramble the Sentence

A 割草 / 里 / 他们 / 院子 / 在

_____

B 在 / 收拾 / 炉子 / 弟弟

_____

C 干活 / 不 / 喜欢 / 厨房 / 我 / 在

_____

D 洗 / 烘干 / 要 / 完 / 衣服

_____

2 填空 Tiánkòng / Fill in the Blank

收拾　冰箱　铲雪　吸地　割草

A 吃剩下的食物要放到_____里面。

B 弟弟把洋芋片掉在地上了，快过来_____。

C 今天是周末了，我们来一起_____屋子吧。

D 又下大雪了，明天早晨需要早起_____。

E 我最不喜欢干的室外家务是_____。

22 Unit 1 Review　　　　真棒 Character Practice Book 3　　　　© EMC Publishing

找出不同 Zhǎochū Bùtóng / *Find the Word that doesn't Belong*

A	冰箱	炉子	烤箱	化妆
B	吸地	铺床	烤肉	洗碗
C	干净	整齐	脏	坏
D	浇花	洗衣服	剪树枝	割草
E	厨余	玻璃	报纸	电池

翻译 Fānyì / *Translation*

A His clothes are so dirty because he doesn't know how to use the washing machine.

_____

B How can your room be so messy? You absolutely must tidy up and vacuum the floor!

_____

C The leaves in autumn are so beautiful, some are yellow and some are red.

_____

D Everybody needs to help shovel snow, so no one will get too tired.

_____

名字: _____ 日期: _____

汉字练习 Hànzì Liànxí / Character Practice

A

Radical	Traditional / Simplified	Pinyin / Meaning	Combination / Meaning
	救		

Stroke Order and Practice Writing

一　寸　寸　寸　求　求　求　救

救　救

救　救

B

Radical	Traditional / Simplified	Pinyin / Meaning	Combination / Meaning
	者		

Stroke Order and Practice Writing

一　土　耂　者　者　者　者

者　者

C

Radical	Traditional / Simplified	Pinyin / Meaning	Combination / Meaning
	银		

Stroke Order and Practice Writing

丿 𠂊 𠂉 𠂎 钅 钅 钅 钅 银 银

银 银

D

Radical	Traditional / Simplified	Pinyin / Meaning	Combination / Meaning
	作		

Stroke Order and Practice Writing

丿 亻 亻 作 作 作 作

作 作

E

Radical	Traditional	Simplified	Pinyin / Meaning	Combination / Meaning
	員	员		

Stroke Order and Practice Writing

丶 丷 口 尸 尸 员 员

员	员					

F

Radical	Traditional / Simplified	Pinyin / Meaning	Combination / Meaning
	演		

Stroke Order and Practice Writing

丶 丶 氵 氵 氵 沪 沪 沪

淯 淯 渖 演 演

演	演					

名字: _____ 日期: _____

G

Radical	Traditional	Simplified	Pinyin / Meaning	Combination / Meaning
	藝	艺		

Stroke Order and Practice Writing

一 十 艹 艺

艺 艺

H

Radical	Traditional	Simplified	Pinyin / Meaning	Combination / Meaning
	獸	兽		

Stroke Order and Practice Writing

丶 丷 丷 兯 兯 単 兽 兽 兽 兽

兽 兽

© EMC Publishing 真棒 Character Practice Book 3 Unit 2 Lesson A 27

I

Radical	Traditional	Simplified	Pinyin / Meaning	Combination / Meaning
	醫	医		

Stroke Order and Practice Writing

一　丅　万　互　歪　矢　医

医　医

J

Radical	Traditional	Simplified	Pinyin / Meaning	Combination / Meaning
	護	护		

Stroke Order and Practice Writing

一　扌　扌　扩　护　护

护　护

2 听写 Tīngxiě / *Dictation*

A

Pinyin:

B

Pinyin:

3 翻译 Fānyì / *Translation*

A I am a veterinarian and not a medical doctor.

Pinyin:

B Originally, I wanted to be an athlete, but I became a journalist instead.

Pinyin:

4 阅读 **Yuèdú** / *Reading*

张凡： 马上就要毕业了，你打算读什么大学？

赵琳： 我想读医学院，因为我的梦想是做一名医生。

张凡： 医生可是很好的职业啊！但是医学院太贵了。

赵琳： 是啊，我也知道医学院的学费会很贵，所以现在一直都在打工、

攒(*to save*)钱。
zǎn

张凡： 你在哪儿打工呢？

赵琳： 我在我家附近的一家餐厅里，做厨师的助理(*assistant*)。你呢，今后
zhùlǐ

有什么打算(*plan*)？
dǎsuàn

张凡： 我对科学很感兴趣，想读一个和建筑(*architectuaral*)有关的专业，以后
jiànzhù

成为一名工程师。

赵琳： 那我等你学好以后帮我盖(*to build*)一座大房子哦！
gài

Unit 2 Lesson B

名字: _____ 日期: _____

汉字练习 | **Hànzì Liànxí** / *Character Practice*

A

Radical	Traditional	Simplified	Pinyin / Meaning	Combination / Meaning
	簡	简		

Stroke Order and Practice Writing

丿 𠂉 𠂉 𥫗 𥫗 𥫗 竹 竹 竹

简 简 简 简

简 简

B

Radical	Traditional / Simplified	Pinyin / Meaning	Combination / Meaning
	幼		

Stroke Order and Practice Writing

𠃋 幺 幺 幻 幼

幼 幼

C

Radical	Traditional / Simplified	Pinyin / Meaning	Combination / Meaning
	推		

Stroke Order and Practice Writing

一 丁 才 扌 扩 扩 扩 拄 拄

推 推

推 推 | | | | | | |

D

Radical	Traditional / Simplified	Pinyin / Meaning	Combination / Meaning
	研		

Stroke Order and Practice Writing

一 丆 不 石 石 矼 研 研

研 研 | | | | | |

E

Radical	Traditional / Simplified	Pinyin / Meaning	Combination / Meaning
	招		

Stroke Order and Practice Writing

一　丁　才　护　护　招　招　招

招	招						

F

Radical	Traditional	Simplified	Pinyin / Meaning	Combination / Meaning
	軍	军		

Stroke Order and Practice Writing

丶　冖　宀　写　写　军

军	军						

G

Radical	Traditional	Simplified	Pinyin / Meaning	Combination / Meaning
	補	补		

Stroke Order and Practice Writing

丶 ｦ 礻 衤 礻 礼 补

补 补

H

Radical	Traditional	Simplified	Pinyin / Meaning	Combination / Meaning
	薦	荐		

Stroke Order and Practice Writing

一 十 卄 芒 芦 芢 荐 荐

荐 荐

I

Radical	Traditional / Simplified	Pinyin / Meaning	Combination / Meaning
	取		

Stroke Order and Practice Writing

一　丆　丆　耵　耵　耳　耳　取　取

取　取

J

Radical	Traditional	Simplified	Pinyin / Meaning	Combination / Meaning
	畢	毕		

Stroke Order and Practice Writing

一　上　匕　比　毕　毕

毕　毕

名字: _____   日期: _____

2 听写 Tīngxiě / *Dictation*

A

Pinyin:

B

Pinyin:

3 翻译 Fānyì / *Translation*

A You must study for three years in order to graduate.

Pinyin:

B So long as your cram school homework is done, then you may go play basketball.

Pinyin:

真棒 Character Practice Book 3

4 阅读 Yuèdú / Reading

张璐: 你大学申请的怎么样了?

李猛: 我的申请表填完了,学校的成绩单也拿到了,现在在等我的教授给

我写推荐信。

张璐: 推荐信很难写吗?

李猛: 难写倒不是很难写,但是教授都很忙,需要等他们有空的时候。

而且我需要三封推荐信,需要找三位不同的教授来写。

张璐: 听起来申请学校比申请工作还要复杂(complicated)啊。
　　　　　　　　　　　　　　　　　　　fùzá

李猛: 是啊,你在找工作吗?

张璐: 对啊,已经面试过好几家公司了,现在就在等着结果了,好紧张

啊,我天天都要查我的邮箱。

李猛: 别紧张,你这么出色(outstanding)一定会被录取的。祝你好运!
　　　　　　　　　　chūsè

张璐: 我也希望是,谢谢你。

Unit 2 Review

1 句子重组 Jùzi Chóngzǔ / *Unscramble the Sentence*

A 我 / 救火员 / 的 / 梦想 / 成为 / 一名 / 是

_____

B 写 / 申请 / 推荐信 / 需要 / 大学

_____

C 我 / 作家 / 当 / 以后 / 毕业 / 想

_____

D 了 / 真 / 你 / 被 / 高兴 / 研究所 / 录取 / 那家

_____

2 填空 Tiánkòng / *Fill in the Blank*

| 医生 银行 兽医 简历 幼儿园 演员 |

A 我要把钱存到_____里面去。

B 他是我最喜欢的电影_____。

C _____是给人看病的，_____是给动物看病的。

D 我不记得我_____时发生的事情了。

E 要找工作了，可是我从来没有写过_____。

3 找出不同 Zhǎochū Bùtóng / *Find the Word that doesn't Belong*

A	公寓	工程师	运动员	厨师
B	警察	保安	军人	艺术家
C	中学	医学院	幼儿园	小学
D	成绩	简历	入学	推荐信
E	多半	后来	直接	经济

4 翻译 Fānyì / *Translation*

A I love music and I hope to have a job in the music field.

_____

B It's not that I didn't know China's economy is getting strong, I just didn't know it would grow this fast.

_____

C Now that there are many online universities, it should be easy to work parttime and study parttime.

_____

D You're got a cold and need to drink more water.

_____

名字: _____ 日期: _____

汉字练习 **Hànzì Liànxí** / *Character Practice*

A

Radical	Traditional / Simplified	Pinyin / Meaning	Combination / Meaning
	森		

Stroke Order and Practice Writing

一 十 才 木 木 朾 朾 㭀 森

森 森 森

森 森

B

Radical	Traditional	Simplified	Pinyin / Meaning	Combination / Meaning
	車	车		

Stroke Order and Practice Writing

一 ナ 仨 车

车 车

真棒 Character Practice Book 3

C

Radical	Traditional / Simplified	Pinyin / Meaning	Combination / Meaning
	睡		

Stroke Order and Practice Writing

丨 冂 月 月 目 盯 盯 盯 眍

眻 睡 睡 睡

睡 睡

D

Radical	Traditional / Simplified	Pinyin / Meaning	Combination / Meaning
	屋		

Stroke Order and Practice Writing

⁊ ⁊ 尸 尸 层 层 层 屋 屋

屋 屋

E

Radical	Traditional / Simplified	Pinyin / Meaning	Combination / Meaning
	足		

Stroke Order and Practice Writing

丶 丨口 口 口 足 足 足

足 足

F

Radical	Traditional / Simplified	Pinyin / Meaning	Combination / Meaning
	烤		

Stroke Order and Practice Writing

丶 丷 火 火 灯 灯 炷 烤 烤

烤

烤 烤

G

Radical	Traditional	Simplified	Pinyin / Meaning	Combination / Meaning
	極	极		

Stroke Order and Practice Writing

一　十　才　木　朾　极　极

极　极

H

Radical	Traditional / Simplified	Pinyin / Meaning	Combination / Meaning
	象		

Stroke Order and Practice Writing

ノ　ハ　ク　ク　台　名　兔　象

象　象

象　象

I

Radical	Traditional / Simplified	Pinyin / Meaning	Combination / Meaning
	洲		

Stroke Order and Practice Writing

丶 丶 氵 氵 汁 沙 洲 洲 洲

洲 洲

J

Radical	Traditional / Simplified	Pinyin / Meaning	Combination / Meaning
	洋		

Stroke Order and Practice Writing

丶 丶 氵 氵 汁 泮 洋 洋

洋 洋

2 听写 Tīngxiě / Dictation

A

Pinyin:

B

Pinyin:

3 翻译 Fānyì / Translation

A Wait until after I graduate, then I am going to take a trip to Europe.

Pinyin:

B This bear isn't very big; it is the size of a big dog.

Pinyin:

玛丽: 这个周末你有什么打算?

大卫: 我没有啊,咱们叫 *(to invite)* 上一些好朋友一起去露营吧。
jiào

玛丽: 好主意!这个周末的天气还特别好。你露过营吗?

大卫: 当然,我经常去露营呢。

玛丽: 那就好,那你一定会生火、烤肉、搭帐篷之类的了。

大卫: 这些活我都没问题,但是如果我们只周末去两天的话,

我议建 *(to suggest)* 不要去太远的地方,不要把时间浪费在路上。
jiànyì

离这里不远有个营地,里面有很多漂亮的小木屋可以住。

玛丽: 住小木屋?那我们就不用带帐篷和睡袋了?

大卫: 不用带了,但是我们同样可以钓鱼、打猎、远足和烤肉。

玛丽: 好啊好啊!赶紧去通知 *(to notice)* 我们的朋友吧。
tōngzhī

名字: _____ 日期: _____

A

Radical	Traditional / Simplified	Pinyin / Meaning	Combination / Meaning
	票		

Stroke Order and Practice Writing

一　厂　厅　西　西　西　覀　亜　票

票　票

票　票

B

Radical	Traditional / Simplified	Pinyin / Meaning	Combination / Meaning
	城		

Stroke Order and Practice Writing

一　十　土　圵　圹　坊　城　城　城

城　城

C

Radical	Traditional	Simplified	Pinyin / Meaning	Combination / Meaning
	艙	舱		

Stroke Order and Practice Writing

丶 丿 力 角 角 角 舟 舟 舱

舱

舱 舱

D

Radical	Traditional / Simplified	Pinyin / Meaning	Combination / Meaning
	谷		

Stroke Order and Practice Writing

丶 八 分 父 谷 谷 谷

谷 谷

E

Radical	Traditional / Simplified	Pinyin / Meaning	Combination / Meaning
	宫		

Stroke Order and Practice Writing

丶 宀 宀 宀 宁 宇 宫 宫 宫

宫	宫						

F

Radical	Traditional / Simplified	Pinyin / Meaning	Combination / Meaning
	世		

Stroke Order and Practice Writing

一 卄 世 世

世	世						

G

Radical	Traditional / Simplified	Pinyin / Meaning	Combination / Meaning
	神		

Stroke Order and Practice Writing

丶 　ラ　ネ　ネ　ネ　初　神　神　神

神 神 | | | | |

H

Radical	Traditional / Simplified	Pinyin / Meaning	Combination / Meaning
	租		

Stroke Order and Practice Writing

一　二　千　禾　禾　利　和　租　租

租

租 租 | | | | |

I

Radical	Traditional / Simplified	Pinyin / Meaning	Combination / Meaning
	界		

Stroke Order and Practice Writing

丶　冂　曰　用　田　罗　界　界　界

界　界

J

Radical	Traditional / Simplified	Pinyin / Meaning	Combination / Meaning
	套		

Stroke Order and Practice Writing

一　ナ　大　太　本　本　套　套　套

套

套　套

2. 听写 Tīngxiě / *Dictation*

A

Pinyin:

B

Pinyin:

3. 翻译 Fānyì / *Translation*

A Only in the case that you don't like animals, otherwise we must go to Sea World.

Pinyin:

B The Grand Canyon is beautiful, and there are not too many tourists.

Pinyin:

小花: 小红，你回来啦！去美国玩得怎么样？

小红: 我去那边玩得很好，美国好玩的东西很多。

小花: 你去了多久？

小红: 我去了三个礼拜，可是还是感觉(*to feel*)时间不够用，很多地方都
　　　　　　　　　　　　　　　gǎnjué
没去。

小花: 快跟我说说你的行程。

小红: 我们先飞到美国西海岸的洛杉矶，去了迪斯尼乐园和好莱坞。然

后开车到圣地亚哥，那里有好玩的海洋世界。之后我们又开车到

了拉斯维加斯，路上参观了大峡谷。参观完拉斯维加斯，我们飞

到了东海岸的纽约，看到了自由女神。然后又坐火车到了华盛顿，

看到了白宫。

小花: 你几乎把美国都转遍(*to travel all around*)了啊！
　　　　　　　　　　　zhuàn biàn

小红: 南边的迈阿密和奥兰多这次没有时间去了。

小花: 那也很不错了，我有机会也一定要去美国玩。

Unit 3 Review

名字: _____ 日期: _____

A 森林 / 吧 / 一起 / 下个 / 我们 / 去 / 里 / 远足 / 月

_____

B 我 / 小木屋 / 喜欢 / 不 / 睡

_____

C 我 / 的 / 订 / 一张 / 机票 / 请 / 经济舱 / 帮

_____

D 看不到 / 世界 / 两极 / 地图上 / 我 / 怎么 / 这张

_____

2 填空 Tiánkòng / *Fill in the Blank*

露营车　大象　洋　自由女神　洲　租车　华盛顿

A 在动物园里能看到很多种动物，可我最喜欢_____。

B 我露营的时候住过小木屋和帐篷，可是从来没有住过_____。

C 世界上有七大_____和五大_____。

D _____在纽约，白宫在_____。

E 到了那个旅游城市，我们需要_____。

3 找出不同 Zhǎochū Bùtóng / *Find the Word that doesn't Belong*

A	帐篷	小木屋	老虎	露营车
B	科威特	洛杉矶	以色列	利比亚
C	亚洲	欧洲	非洲	公园
D	平房	普通房	单人房	标准房
E	黄石公园	大峡谷	好莱坞	尼加拉瀑布

4 翻译 Fānyì / *Translation*

A You will certainly like this state park; it's similar to a forest.

_____

B If it were not for the field trip I never would have learned how to start a fire.

_____

C There are no words to explain how beautiful this scenic spot is, especially during peak season.

_____

D Law School is too expensive; I will have to wait until I have enough money saved.

_____

Unit 4 Lesson A

名字: _____ 日期: _____

A

Radical	Traditional / Simplified	Pinyin / Meaning	Combination / Meaning
	著		

Stroke Order and Practice Writing

一 十 艹 艹 芏 芏 芋 莟 著 著

著	著						

B

Radical	Traditional / Simplified	Pinyin / Meaning	Combination / Meaning
	诗		

Stroke Order and Practice Writing

丶 讠 讠 讦 诖 诘 诗 诗

诗	诗						

C

Radical	Traditional / Simplified	Pinyin / Meaning	Combination / Meaning
	霜		

Stroke Order and Practice Writing

一 厂 户 乖 乖 乖 雨 雨 雪

雫 雱 霏 霜 霜 霜 霜 霜

霜 霜

D

Radical	Traditional	Simplified	Pinyin / Meaning	Combination / Meaning
	溫	温		

Stroke Order and Practice Writing

丶 冫 氵 沪 沪 沪 沪 沪

温 温 温

温 温

E

Radical	Traditional / Simplified	Pinyin / Meaning	Combination / Meaning
	欣		

Stroke Order and Practice Writing

丶　丿　厂　斤　斤'　斤ﾉ　欣　欣

欣　欣

F

Radical	Traditional / Simplified	Pinyin / Meaning	Combination / Meaning
	散		

Stroke Order and Practice Writing

一　十　廿　芈　芢　芀　昔　昔

散　散　散

散　散

G

Radical	Traditional / Simplified	Pinyin / Meaning	Combination / Meaning
	秀		

Stroke Order and Practice Writing

丿　二　千　禾　禾　秀　秀

秀　秀

H

Radical	Traditional	Simplified	Pinyin / Meaning	Combination / Meaning
	劇	剧		

Stroke Order and Practice Writing

⁊　⁊　尸　尸　尸　尽　居　居　居

剧

剧　剧

I

Radical	Traditional / Simplified	Pinyin / Meaning	Combination / Meaning
	舞		

Stroke Order and Practice Writing

丿 ⺊ 乇 午 缶 無 無 舞

舞 舞 舞 舞 舞

舞 舞

J

Radical	Traditional	Simplified	Pinyin / Meaning	Combination / Meaning
	賞	赏		

Stroke Order and Practice Writing

丶 ⺊ ⺊ ⺌ 屵 屵 尚 尚 尚

赏 赏 赏

赏 赏

2 听写 Tīngxiě / *Dictation*

A

Pinyin:

B

Pinyin:

3 翻译 Fānyì / *Translation*

A We are going to have a talent show at school.

Pinyin:

B I am willing to read any author of prose.

Pinyin:

4 阅读 Yuèdú / Reading

李磊: 王龙，你也在图书馆呢？

王龙: 嗨，李磊，我在这里准备(to prepare)明天的考试呢，你也来学习么？
zhùnbèi

李磊: 不是，我是来借几本书。

王龙: 你想借什么书？

李磊: 我最近对中国文学特别感兴趣，想找几本中国经典文学的书。

王龙: 那我推荐(to recommend)你读一读中国最著名的"四大名著"。
tuījiàn

李磊: 我听说过"四大名著"，你觉得里面的哪一本书最有趣(interesting)呢？
qù

王龙: 我喜欢"三国演义"这本书，里面有很多打仗(war)的故事。
zhàng

李磊: 好，那我就先借这本书吧，谢谢你的建议(suggestion)。
jiànyì

王龙: 不客气，再见。

真棒 Character Practice Book 3

名字: _____   日期: _____

汉字练习 Hànzì Liànxí / *Character Practice*

A

Radical	Traditional / Simplified	Pinyin / Meaning	Combination / Meaning
	蜜		

Stroke Order and Practice Writing

丶 八 宀 宀 宓 宓 宓 宓 宓
宓 宓 宻 蜜 蜜

蜜 蜜

B

Radical	Traditional	Simplified	Pinyin / Meaning	Combination / Meaning
	殼	壳		

Stroke Order and Practice Writing

一 十 士 声 声 壳 壳

壳 壳

C

Radical	Traditional / Simplified	Pinyin / Meaning	Combination / Meaning
	蚊		

Stroke Order and Practice Writing

丶 冖 口 中 虫 虫 虻 蚊 蚊

蚊

蚊	蚊						

D

Radical	Traditional	Simplified	Pinyin / Meaning	Combination / Meaning
	靈	灵		

Stroke Order and Practice Writing

㇕ ㄱ ㄱ ㄱ 灵 灵 灵

灵	灵					

E

Radical	Traditional	Simplified	Pinyin / Meaning	Combination / Meaning
	誠	诚		

Stroke Order and Practice Writing

丶　讠　讠　讠　讠　诚　诚　诚

诚	诚						

F

Radical	Traditional / Simplified		Pinyin / Meaning	Combination / Meaning
	笑			

Stroke Order and Practice Writing

丿　仁　仁　竹　竹　竹　竺　竺　竿

笑

笑	笑						

G

Radical	Traditional / Simplified	Pinyin / Meaning	Combination / Meaning
	底		

Stroke Order and Practice Writing

丶 亠 广 广 庄 庄 底 底

底 底

H

Radical	Traditional / Simplified	Pinyin / Meaning	Combination / Meaning
	管		

Stroke Order and Practice Writing

丿 ㇏ ㇏ ㄠ 竹 竹 竹 竹 竹

管 管 管 管 管

管 管

I

Radical	Traditional / Simplified	Pinyin / Meaning	Combination / Meaning
	昆		

Stroke Order and Practice Writing

丶 冂 冃 日 旦 昆 昆 昆

昆	昆						

J

Radical	Traditional / Simplified	Pinyin / Meaning	Combination / Meaning
	根		

Stroke Order and Practice Writing

一 十 才 木 朾 栌 杈 根 根

根

根	根						

2 听写 Tīngxiě / *Dictation*

A

Pinyin:

B

Pinyin:

3 翻译 Fānyì / *Translation*

A If it's not all mosquitos, it's the bees in the cabin.

Pinyin:

B He is not a sincere person at all.

Pinyin:

真棒 Character Practice Book 3

4 阅读 **Yuèdú** / *Reading*

山姆: 你读过中国小说"梁山伯和祝英台"的故事么?

露西: 我没有听说过,里面是讲什么的?

山姆: 讲的是两个人的爱情故事,但是他们不能在一起,后来两个人都变成蝴蝶,一起飞走了。

露西: 变成蝴蝶?为什么不是别的昆虫呢?像蜜蜂、蜻蜓、萤火虫之类的?

山姆: 这个我就不知道了,你要去问作者吧,不过你的想法真的很有趣,反应也很敏捷。

露西: 我经常会有一些很奇怪(strange)的想法,我的朋友都说我机灵。
　　　　　　　　　　　　　　　qíguài

山姆: 我没有你这么机灵,我觉得我很迟钝。

露西: 没有啦,我觉得你很诚恳也很热心。

Unit 4 Review

1 句子重组 Jùzi Chóngzǔ / Unscramble the Sentence

A 周末 / 看 / 这个 / 一起 / 我们 / 吧 / 演唱会 / 去

_____

B 中国 / 你 / 的 / 吗 / 四大名著 / 知道

_____

C 冬天 / 没有 / 的 / 雪 / 这里

_____

D 吗 / 想要 / 脱口秀 / 参加 / 你 / 节目

_____

2 填空 Tiánkòng / Fill in the Blank

| 四大名著　热情　蟑螂　宋词　希腊悲剧　性别　唐诗 |

A 很多昆虫我都不喜欢，但我最害怕的昆虫是_____。

B 我的性格很_____，喜欢和陌生人说话。

C 中国古典文学有_____，西方著名的文学有_____。

D 中国古代的文学体裁多种多样，最有名的是_____和
_____。

E 他是男的还是女的？我看不出他的_____。

3 找出不同 Zhǎochū Bùtóng / *Find the Word that doesn't Belong*

A 水浒传   奥兰多   三国演义   西游记

B 古典   热心   诚恳   有趣

C 蚊子   苍蝇   蜜蜂   蚂蚁

D 雪   冰   雨   霜

E 歌剧   话剧   演唱会   音乐会

4 翻译 Fānyì / *Translation*

A If you want to be good at cross talk, one way is to study the language, another way is to have courage.

_____

B For me, Roman myth is more interesting than Greek tragedies.

_____

C I run very fast, my classmates all call me "Rabbit".

_____

D No matter what difficulties come along, I will help you.

_____

名字: _____ 日期: _____

汉字练习 Hànzì Liànxí / *Character Practice*

A

Radical	Traditional / Simplified	Pinyin / Meaning	Combination / Meaning
	零		

Stroke Order and Practice Writing

一 厂 广 广 雨 雨 雨 雨 雨

雵 雯 零 零

零 零

B

Radical	Traditional	Simplified	Pinyin / Meaning	Combination / Meaning
	環	环		

Stroke Order and Practice Writing

一 二 干 王 玎 环 环

环 环

C

Radical	Traditional / Simplified	Pinyin / Meaning	Combination / Meaning
	染		

Stroke Order and Practice Writing

丶 丶 氵 氿 氿 染 染 染 染

染 染

D

Radical	Traditional / Simplified	Pinyin / Meaning	Combination / Meaning
	保		

Stroke Order and Practice Writing

丿 亻 亻 保 保 保 保 保 保

保 保

E

Radical	Traditional	Simplified	Pinyin / Meaning	Combination / Meaning
	類	类		

Stroke Order and Practice Writing

丶 丷 丷 半 半 米 癶 癶 类

类	类						

F

Radical	Traditional	Simplified	Pinyin / Meaning	Combination / Meaning
	撿	捡		

Stroke Order and Practice Writing

一 丁 扌 扩 扲 捡 捡 捡 捡

捡

捡	捡						

G

Radical	Traditional / Simplified	Pinyin / Meaning	Combination / Meaning
	食		

Stroke Order and Practice Writing

丿 人 人 今 今 今 食 食 食

食 食

H

Radical	Traditional / Simplified	Pinyin / Meaning	Combination / Meaning
	借		

Stroke Order and Practice Writing

丿 亻 亻 仁 㐾 供 借 借 借
借

借 借

I

Radical	Traditional / Simplified	Pinyin / Meaning	Combination / Meaning
	物		

Stroke Order and Practice Writing

丿 ㇒ 牜 牛 牛 牞 物 物

物 物

J

Radical	Traditional / Simplified	Pinyin / Meaning	Combination / Meaning
	污		

Stroke Order and Practice Writing

丶 冫 氵 汸 汚 污

污 污

2 听写 Tīngxiě / *Dictation*

A

Pinyin:

B

Pinyin:

3 翻译 Fānyì / *Translation*

A Ever since I became fat, I no longer eat snacks.

Pinyin:

B I do not lend money to friends.

Pinyin:

4 阅读 **Yuèdú** *Reading*

王刚: 又堵车(*traffic jam*)！真烦人。
　　　　　dǔ

徐强: 是啊，路上的车越来越多，交通状况(*situation*)也越来越差。
　　　　　　　　　　　　　　　　　　zhuàngkuàng

王刚: 污染也变得严重了，天空都是灰色的。

徐强: 看看这么多车排出的尾气(*vehicle emission*)，都是空气污染啊。
　　　　　　　　　　　　　wěi

王刚: 还有的司机很心急，总在鸣笛(*to honk*)，也造成了一种噪音污染。
　　　　　　　　　　míngdí

徐强: 我们的城市发展得很快，但是负面影响(*negative influence*)也是很多的。
　　　　　　　　　　　　　　　fùmiàn yǐngxiǎng

　　　　还记得我家门前那条河，我小时候总在里面游泳，但是现在都不

　　　　敢了。

徐强: 那边开了好几家化工厂，废水都直接排入到了河里，味道可难闻了！

王刚: 我们只有一个地球，每个人都应该关注环保。

Unit 5 Lesson B

名字: ______________________ 日期: __________

1 汉字练习 Hànzì Liànxí / *Character Practice*

A

Radical	Traditional / Simplified	Pinyin / Meaning	Combination / Meaning
	恩		

Stroke Order and Practice Writing

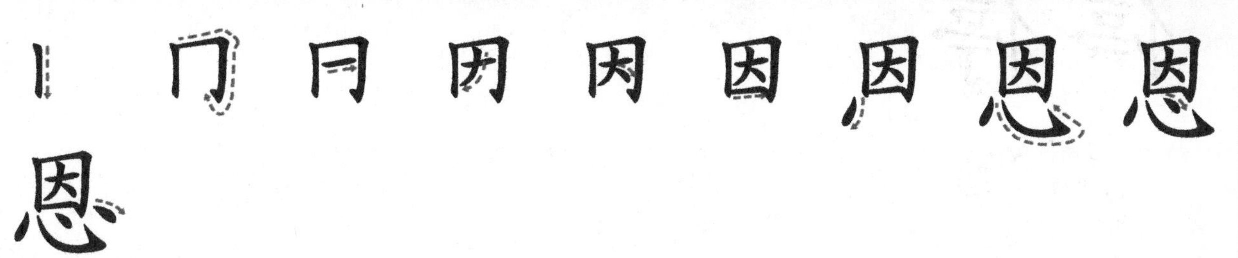

恩	恩							

B

Radical	Traditional	Simplified	Pinyin / Meaning	Combination / Meaning
	費	费		

Stroke Order and Practice Writing

费	费							

C

Radical	Traditional / Simplified	Pinyin / Meaning	Combination / Meaning
	停		

Stroke Order and Practice Writing

丿 亻 彳 广 庁 停 停 停 停 停 停

停	停						

D

Radical	Traditional	Simplified	Pinyin / Meaning	Combination / Meaning
	線	线		

Stroke Order and Practice Writing

纟 纟 纟 纟 纟 线 线 线

线	线						

E

Radical	Traditional	Simplified	Pinyin / Meaning		Combination / Meaning
	險	险			

Stroke Order and Practice Writing

阝 阝 阝 阝 阸 险 险 险 险

险 险

F

Radical	Traditional / Simplified	Pinyin / Meaning		Combination / Meaning
	念			

Stroke Order and Practice Writing

丿 人 人 今 念 念 念

念 念

G

Radical	Traditional / Simplified	Pinyin / Meaning	Combination / Meaning
	青		

Stroke Order and Practice Writing

一　二　キ　キ　青　青　青　青

青	青				

H

Radical	Traditional	Simplified	Pinyin / Meaning	Combination / Meaning
	紀	纪		

Stroke Order and Practice Writing

乚　纟　纟　纟　纟　纪

纪	纪				

名字: _____ 日期: _____

I

Radical	Traditional	Simplified	Pinyin / Meaning	Combination / Meaning
	聖	圣		

Stroke Order and Practice Writing

フ　又　圣　圣　圣

圣　圣

J

Radical	Traditional	Simplified	Pinyin / Meaning	Combination / Meaning
	慶	庆		

Stroke Order and Practice Writing

丶　亠　广　庐　庐　庆

庆　庆

名字: _____ 日期: _____

2 听写 Tīngxiě / *Dictation*

A

Pinyin:

B

Pinyin:

3 翻译 Fānyì / *Translation*

A You can celebrate Thanksgiving with my family.

Pinyin:

B The parking fee is affected by the Christmas holiday.

Pinyin:

真棒 Character Practice Book 3

妈妈： 这个月的账单来了，一共两千多块。

爸爸： 怎么这么多钱？都有什么费用？

妈妈： 红红交学费就交了一千块，剩下的还有电话费、网络费、有线电视

费、瓦斯费和电费。

爸爸： 哦对了，咱们的汽车保险(*insurance*)就要到期了，还要买保险。
bǎoxiǎn

妈妈： 好，这个我记下了。此外下个月就是儿童节了，咱们要给红红买礼物。

爸爸： 你想好给她买什么了吗？

妈妈： 我觉得她很喜欢衣服，我就给她买一件衣服吧。

爸爸： 那我带她去她最喜欢的餐厅吃饭。

妈妈： 好主意。

Unit 5 Review

名字: _____ 日期: _____

 **句子重组** **Jùzi Chóngzǔ** / *Unscramble the Sentence*

A　对 / 重要 / 地球 / 很 / 环保

_____

B　起来 / 随手 / 垃圾 / 我们 / 捡 / 地上 / 的 / 要

_____

C　说话 / 也是 / 污染 / 一种 / 噪音 / 大声

_____

D　高 / 月 / 很 / 的 / 这个 / 电话费

_____

2 **填空** **Tiánkòng** / *Fill in the Blank*

| 资源　零食　塑料袋　儿童节　停车费　妇女节　工业革命 |

A　使用_____很不环保。

B　我喜欢一边看电视，一边吃_____。

C　三月八日是_____，六月一日是_____。

D　车子停在这里需要付_____。

E　从_____以后，地球上的_____就越来越少。

3 找出不同 Zhǎochū Bùtóng / *Find the Word that doesn't Belong*

A   水污染   噪音污染   空气污染   环保

B   国庆节   儿童节   感恩节   妇女节

C   零食   点心   小吃   乳制品

D   瓦斯   纸袋   回收   绿化

E   电话费   旅费   网络费   电费

4 翻译 Fānyì / *Translation*

A   Tonight everyone is going to eat a big meal together. Why are you eating snacks now?

_____

B   Ever since I learned that car insurance is expensive, I no longer want to buy a car.

_____

C   I never want to use so much electricity to celebrate Christmas again.

_____

D   Rather than paying so much money for gas, it's better to carpool.

_____

名字: _____ 日期: _____

汉字练习 Hànzì Liànxí / *Character Practice*

A

Radical	Traditional / Simplified	Pinyin / Meaning	Combination / Meaning
	湖		

Stroke Order and Practice Writing

丶 丶 氵 汁 汁 汁 沽 沽 湖

湖 湖 湖

湖 湖

B

Radical	Traditional / Simplified	Pinyin / Meaning	Combination / Meaning
	池		

Stroke Order and Practice Writing

丶 丶 氵 氵 汕 池

池 池

C

Radical	Traditional / Simplified	Pinyin / Meaning	Combination / Meaning
	原		

Stroke Order and Practice Writing

一 厂 厂 厂 厅 盾 盾 原 原
原

原	原						

D

Radical	Traditional / Simplified	Pinyin / Meaning	Combination / Meaning
	河		

Stroke Order and Practice Writing

丶 冫 氵 汀 汀 河 河 河

河	河						

E

Radical	Traditional / Simplified	Pinyin / Meaning	Combination / Meaning
	江		

Stroke Order and Practice Writing

丶　丶　氵　氵　汀　江

江　江

F

Radical	Traditional	Simplified	Pinyin / Meaning	Combination / Meaning
	鐵	铁		

Stroke Order and Practice Writing

丿　𠂉　𠂉　钅　钅　钅　钅　铁

铁

铁　铁

G

Radical	Traditional / Simplified	Pinyin / Meaning	Combination / Meaning
	沙		

Stroke Order and Practice Writing

丶　丶　氵　氵丿　沙丿　沙丿　沙

沙	沙						

H

Radical	Traditional	Simplified	Pinyin / Meaning	Combination / Meaning
	隨	随		

Stroke Order and Practice Writing

彐　阝　阝一　阝ナ　阝ナ　隋　隋　隋

随　随

随	随					

I

Radical	Traditional	Simplified	Pinyin / Meaning	Combination / Meaning
	輪	轮		

Stroke Order and Practice Writing

一　　ナ　　ナ　　车　　轩　　轩　　轮　　轮

轮　轮

J

Radical	Traditional	Simplified	Pinyin / Meaning	Combination / Meaning
	區	区		

Stroke Order and Practice Writing

一　　丁　　又　　区

区　区

2 听写 Tīngxiě / Dictation

A

Pinyin:

B

Pinyin:

3 翻译 Fānyì / Translation

A My country is small and mostly filled with desert. There aren't many rivers.

Pinyin:

B One third of China is flatlands.

Pinyin:

4 阅读 **Yuèdú** / *Reading*

刘明:　听说你去新疆玩了?
　　　　　　　　　xīnjiāng

王倩:　是啊,我上个月才回来的。

刘明:　那边好玩吗?

王倩:　那边的风景很美,有很多漂亮的湖和美丽的大草原,还有雪山呢。

刘明:　听起来很不错,那边的污染情况怎么样?

王倩:　那边没有一点污染,和大城市里面的感觉完全不同。不过交通有点

　　　　不方便,很多时间都需要走路或者坐三轮车,那边没有地铁,就连

　　　　汽车也很少。

刘明:　你是怎么去的?

王倩:　我是先做飞机,然后再坐火车。花了我16个小时才到的,不过我觉

　　　　得很值。

刘明:　你有没有爬雪山呢?
　　　　　　　　　　pá

王倩:　没有,那个需要训练(*to train*)的,我可爬不上去。不过我照了几张照
　　　　　　　　　　　　　xùnliàn

　　　　片,给你看看。

刘明:　好啊!

名字: _____   日期: _____

汉字练习 **Hànzì Liànxí** / *Character Practice*

A

Radical	Traditional / Simplified	Pinyin / Meaning	Combination / Meaning
	器		

Stroke Order and Practice Writing

丶　口　口　叩　叩　叩　叩　罗　哭

哭　哭　哭　哭　哭　器　器

器　器

B

Radical	Traditional / Simplified	Pinyin / Meaning	Combination / Meaning
	板		

Stroke Order and Practice Writing

一　十　才　木　札　板　板　板

板　板

C

Radical	Traditional	Simplified	Pinyin / Meaning	Combination / Meaning
	鲜	鲜		

Stroke Order and Practice Writing

丿 ⺈ ⺈ 刍 刍 角 鱼 鱼 鱼

鱼ˊ 鲜 鲜 鲜 鲜

鲜	鲜						

D

Radical	Traditional	Simplified	Pinyin / Meaning	Combination / Meaning
	勞	劳		

Stroke Order and Practice Writing

一 ⺮ ⺿ ⺿ 芦 芌 劳

劳	劳						

E

Radical	Traditional	Simplified	Pinyin / Meaning	Combination / Meaning
	沖	冲		

Stroke Order and Practice Writing

丶　冫　冫　汀　冮　冲

冲	冲							

F

Radical	Traditional / Simplified	Pinyin / Meaning	Combination / Meaning
	筒		

Stroke Order and Practice Writing

丿　⺮　⺈　竹　竹　竹　竹　筒　筒

筒　筒　筒

筒	筒					

G

Radical	Traditional	Simplified	Pinyin / Meaning	Combination / Meaning
	夾	夹		

Stroke Order and Practice Writing

一　一　⼉　⼉　乑　夹

夹　夹

H

Radical	Traditional	Simplified	Pinyin / Meaning	Combination / Meaning
	燈	灯		

Stroke Order and Practice Writing

丶　丷　ソ　火　灯　灯

灯　灯

I

Radical	Traditional / Simplified	Pinyin / Meaning	Combination / Meaning
	架		

Stroke Order and Practice Writing

フ	力	加	加	加	架	架	架	架

架	架							

J

Radical	Traditional / Simplified	Pinyin / Meaning	Combination / Meaning
	布		

Stroke Order and Practice Writing

一	ナ	木	布	布

布	布							

名字: _____ 日期: _____

2 听写 Tīngxiě / *Dictation*

A

Pinyin:

B

Pinyin:

3 翻译 Fānyì / *Translation*

A   Compared to me, he is diligent.

Pinyin:

B   She will not be able to finish this work without a flashlight.

Pinyin:

真棒 Character Practice Book 3

4 阅读 **Yuèdú** / *Reading*

汤姆：　中国发展得可真快，尤其是制造业(manufacturing)，现在市场上很多的
　　　　　　　　　　　　　　　zhìzàoyè
　　　　东西都是中国制造。

杰西：　是啊，尤其是一些家用品，像我家的保鲜盒、衣架、电灯泡都是中
　　　　国制造的呢。

汤姆：　你认识从中国来的朋友吗？

杰西：　我认识几个交换学生。

汤姆：　你觉得他们的性格怎么样？

杰西：　首先我觉得他们都很谦虚，对待人很有礼貌。他们也非常的勤劳、
　　　　刻苦，他们的学习成绩都很好。但是有时候他们有些古板、谨慎，
　　　　不善于表现自己，这一点和你差很远啊。

汤姆：　我也觉得这是我的优点，你没发现我还很幽默吗？

杰西：　刚说你一句你就开始骄傲了。

汤姆：　没有啦，和你开个玩笑。

Unit 6 Review

句子重组 Jùzi Chóngzǔ / Unscramble the Sentence

A 坐 / 去 / 那个 / 我 / 城市 / 高速铁路 / 要

_____

B 骑过 / 他 / 没有 / 三轮车 / 从来

_____

C 有个 / 我 / 池塘 / 的 / 院子 / 里面 / 家

_____

D 抹布 / 清理 / 用 / 要 / 厨房

_____

填空 Tiánkòng / Fill in the Blank

保鲜盒　草原　地铁　海边　沙漠

A 今年暑假，我要去_____游泳。

B _____里面又干又热，没人能在里面生活。

C 绿绿的_____上有好多的牛和羊啊！

D 这个城市的交通很方便，我每天坐_____上下班。

E 服务员，请你把这个菜放进_____里。

3 找出不同 Zhǎochū Bùtóng / *Find the Word that doesn't Belong*

A 高速铁路　　自行车　　火车　　汽车

B 沙漠　　高山　　河流　　高原

C 菜板　　树叶　　夹子　　衣架

D 东部　　西部　　上部　　南部

E 自大　　幽默　　谨慎　　温柔

4 翻译 Fānyì / *Translation*

A Even if the lake were not that big, we should not try to swim without an older brother here.

_____

B This city's subway is comfortable, and the ticket is really cheap.

_____

C Compared to others, my older sister is a very proud person.

_____

D My new house is in the middle of construction.

_____

精益求精　**Jīng Yì Qiú Jīng** / *Practice Makes Perfect*

名字: _____ 日期: _____

精益求精 **Jīng Yì Qiú Jīng** / *Practice Makes Perfect*

精益求精 **Jīng Yì Qiú Jīng** / *Practice Makes Perfect*

真棒 Character Practice Book 3

名字: _____ 日期: _____

名字: _____ 日期: _____

精益求精 **Jīng Yì Qiú Jīng** / *Practice Makes Perfect*